THE COMPLETELY MISLEADING GUIDE TO SCHOOL

THE COMPLETELY MISLEADING GUIDE TO SCHOOL

Jim Eldridge

Illustrated by
David Woodward

RED FOX

A Red Fox Book
Published by Arrow Books Limited
20 Vauxhall Bridge Road, London SW1V 2SA

An imprint of the Random Century Group

London Melbourne Sydney Auckland
Johannesburg and agencies throughout the world

First published 1990

Set in Century Schoolbook
by JH Graphics Ltd, Reading

Made and printed in Great Britain
by Courier International Ltd
Tiptree, Essex

ISBN 0 09 970250 9

CONTENTS:

SCHOOLS

Schools come in all different sizes and, frankly, they can be pretty terrifying places. There are two reasons for this:

1. The other children
2. The staff (teachers, caretakers, cooks, etc)

How to deal with other children

Bullies

Bullies are those awful people who roam around the school bashing people. Everyone is terrified of them, including the teachers. There is only one real way to deal with a bully and that is to hire the

7

Mafia, the KGB, MI5 and the CIA to bump him
or her off. However, as even these organizations
are terrified of most bullies, this very rarely works.
So here are some other techniques.

Technique 1: appealing to a bully's conscience
Do this with phrases like 'Please don't hit me, I am an orphan' and 'My pet budgie just died.' Frankly, this is a waste of time as bullies do not have a conscience and will just hit you anyway.

Technique 2: Threats This means saying things like 'My father/brother/sister/mother is Karate champion of the world and if you touch me, he/she will tear your arms and legs off and tie them around your neck.' The problem with this is that it is based on a lie, and as the chances are that the bully will know your family it is unlikely that this story will be believed, particularly if you have a normal family (i.e. weedy with muscles like gnat's knees).

Technique 3: Bribery E.g. 'If you don't hit me I shall give you this bag of sweets and all my other worldly possessions.' As this is what the bully is often after in the first place this is a fairly useless ploy.

Technique 4: Frightening bullies This can be done by falling over when they hit you and pretending to be dead. In theory this should make them panic so much they will never hit you again. In practice this often fails for the following reasons:

1. Bullies haven't got a brain so they can't think to panic. They also couldn't care if you *are* dead.

9

2. It means holding your breath for an awfully long time while you pretend to be dead. As bullies have no brains and are therefore very slow thinkers, it will take them hours of watching you to work out if you are still breathing. After two hours of holding your breath to convince them, you really will be dead.

Technique 5: Humour Distract the bullies' attacks on you by making them laugh. Unfortunately, because bullies don't have a brain, any joke which requires any intelligence whatsoever won't work. The only thing a bully laughs at is people falling over or having great weights dropped on their heads and hurting themselves. So, you could always drop a weight on your head and hurt yourself. This will make the bully laugh, but it is a bit pointless as you still get hurt.

So, if none of these ploys are any use at all, what is the answer? There is only one solution:

Technique 6: Avoid bullies

How to deal with the other children who are not bullies

Gangs or groups

You cannot win with this one. Whichever gang or group you join, all the others will be better than yours with more interesting children in them. The answer is to start your own gang. The trouble is all the really uninteresting kids will join it, as well as all the other kids who've got thrown out of other gangs, and it will soon be such a collection of rejects that you will be forced to leave and be on your own again.

Kids who make fun of you

If you are a genius or even vaguely clever, or wear glasses or have a funny name, then the other kids will make fun of you. This is because they are jealous. The way to deal with them is with a brilliantly cutting, witty reply that they can't answer. Something along the lines of 'Smelly feet!' (However, before doing this check on the size of their fists. If they are unusually large, then say something like 'Yes?, you're quite right, I am an idiot,' and walk away as quickly as possible.)

Learning to live with the staff

1. *Teachers*

(See Chapter 3 on 'Teachers')

2. *School cooks*

(See Chapter 9 on 'School Meals')

3. *School caretakers*

Forget the fact that the head teacher is supposed to be the adult in charge, school caretakers are the people who really run a school.

School caretakers are born into the job. When they are tiny they are presented with a nappy and a small brown overall. This overall is a special sort that grows as they grow so that they never need to change it. This is why all school caretakers wear a brown overall that has so many stains on it that it is able to stand up all on its own if the caretaker should ever take it off.

School caretakers are also like Superman in that they have a Secret Identity. Underneath their brown overall they are Invisible Man (or Woman)! This means that whenever anything really urgent or an emergency happens in the school and the head teacher shouts 'Quick! Find the caretaker!', the caretaker removes his or her brown overall and immediately vanishes and can't be found.

The school secretary

This is usually someone's mum, and you can bet that she also knows your mum. This means that anything you say or do will be reported to your family immediately. The only defence to this is to discredit your school secretary so that your mum won't believe anything she says about you. The best way to do this is to tell your mum that your school secretary was threatened with the sack because she keeps telling lies about the children, but was only saved from losing her job because she knows a dreadful secret about the head teacher.

The History of School Uniform: how it all began

Woad

A long time ago in Ancient Britain the only thing children used to wear when they went to school was woad. Woad was a blue paint and it came in two sorts: emulsion and gloss.

Emulsion woad was all right but it used to come off whenever it rained, and as it used to rain all the time the Ancient British kids who wore emulsion woad got really fed up. One minute they'd be walking along dressed in their blue woad, the next second a cloud would appear and then a crash! of thunder, pit-a-pat pit-a-pat of raindrops, and there they'd be, stark naked.

Gloss woad did not come off in the rain. The trouble was it didn't come off at all, no matter how often you washed, so once you painted yourself with blue gloss woad that was it, and tough luck if that particular shade of blue went out of fashion in the next ten years.

Another problem with gloss woad was that it took longer to dry. This meant that if ancient schoolkids wore newly painted gloss woad to school then it would still be sticky when they arrived for their lessons. As a result many of them got stuck to the ancient school chairs (made of stone) that they sat on.

Because of this it was decided to replace woad for kids with school uniform made out of skins.

Skin school uniforms

Skin school uniforms came in different designs, depending on which part of the world the school was in. If it was in an area roamed mainly by dragons, or sabre-toothed tigers or mammoths, then that was the skin of the animal that became the school outfit. (Those ancient schoolkids who lived in areas where the only skins available were those of bees, wasps and flies used to get very cold in the winter.)

This idea of using skins worked for a while, until people began to notice that they were running out of animals. Within a few years hundreds of species

of animals that had been used as school uniforms became extinct. These included: the unicorn, the dragon, the lesser-spotted slipwort, the dodo, the hairy grubber, the sabre-toothed tiger, etc etc.

Cloth uniforms

No more animals meant no more skins, so the different ancient schools had to invent cloth instead

for their school clothing. This presented the kids
with a serious problem. As most ancient schoolkids
had the intelligence of a brick they had difficulty
in finding the way to their correct school and had
only found their way by following any other kid
wearing the same sort of skin (e.g. a mammoth).
Once all schoolkids took to wearing just cloth, they
were lost and used to just wander around aimlessly
and turn up at the wrong schools all the time.

To solve this problem, badges were made for each
school with a picture of the animal whose skin they
would have been wearing if there had been any
of those animals left. And that is how the badge
on the school blazer came into being.

Modern school uniform

Modern school uniform is especially designed to
make children look peculiar. This is done by
making the jacket sleeves and the trousers or skirt
far too long, or far too short.

The usual excuse that adults give children when
they stick you in a uniform that is too big is that
you will 'grow into it'. It is a waste of breath
pointing out to them that to grow into it you would
need to reach a height of four metres with arms
and legs three metres long, and have a waist
measurement bigger than the dome of St Paul's

Cathedral. However, remember that if you are given a school uniform which is too big, this is preferable to being given one that is far too small. A uniform that is too small not only looks ridiculous, it can also strangle you.

The other interesting thing about modern school uniforms is that they are made to fall apart. As soon as you walk through the school gates all the stitching will come undone and your sleeves will fall off. The cloth of your trousers or skirt will also immediately start to self-destruct into enormous holes. Yet who gets the blame? Not the idiot who made this ramshackle outfit, but you, the innocent wearer.

TEACHERS

Teachers come in different types: weedy wimps, mad, ultra-strict, etc.

Head teachers

Head teachers are so called because they have their heads with them at all times, as opposed to some teachers who keep losing their heads. Because these head teachers remember to carry their heads with them they are important teachers and are therefore put in charge of the other teachers.

Mad teachers

These have staring eyes and piercing voices and are often found at the front of the class tearing their hair out because a child has dared to ask a question such as 'What's the date?'

Some people think that mad teachers become mad after years and years of teaching, but my own observations show that many new teachers who come into the profession are already at this mad stage when they first walk into a classroom. My advice is: if you go into a class and the teacher is biting bits out of the desks and shouting and waving his or her arms like a windmill with hiccups, make an excuse and go home ill.

Ultra strict teachers

Ultra-strict teachers never shout. They don't need to because their classrooms are always so quiet you can hear a germ drop. If anyone so much as breathes in an ultra-strict teacher's class, then the teacher just has to look at the culprit with eyes like laser beams and the poor offender goes Phffft! and turns into a heap of ashes on the spot.

Ultra-strict teachers are all descended from horror movie monsters like Count Dracula and Frankenstein's Monster, which is why they are able to control a class with the power of sheer terror. Ultra-strict teachers also have the power of telepathy and they know in advance when a pupil is thinking of doing something like writing a rude word on the cover of their exercise book.

Lazy teachers

Lazy teachers don't want to be in a classroom any more than the pupils do. In fact, they want to be in the classroom even less than the pupils and are always finding excuses to be out of it. What usually happens with a lazy teacher is this: you will go into class. The lazy teacher will say: 'Right, get out your books and start reading.' After about two minutes, this teacher will say: 'I've got to go to Mr (or Miss or Mrs) Wotsit about (something or other that is pretty unimportant because the lazy teacher's just made it up). I'll be back in a moment. If I hear any noise coming from this classroom while I'm out there'll be trouble.'

Then the lazy teacher disappears and goes for a quiet rest in the Staff Room until the bell goes for the end of the lesson.

The lazy teacher also sets loads of work to keep you quiet in class, but never looks at it and merely goes to sleep instead.

Lazy teachers can be identified by the cobwebs growing around them from their general lack of movement. This has given rise to stories of many teachers being dead. In some cases this may be true, but it can be easily tested by holding a five pound note near the cobweb surrounding the suspected dead teacher. If a hand comes out from the cobweb and grabs the money, the teacher is still alive. If a hand does not appear, you can safely stop doing the work that has been set.

Wimp teachers

Wimp teachers can usually be found cowering in a corner of the classroom saying 'Don't come near me!' and 'I'm ill!' and such things. Wimp teachers always hope they will get the job of teaching tiny little three-year-olds who wouldn't dream of doing anything naughty. Unfortunately Wimp teachers are usually thrown into classrooms full of three metre tall thugs all aged about fourteen (but looking about thirty) and all armed to the teeth. It is not a lot of fun being a wimp teacher.

How teachers are trained

Many children think that teachers choose the job they do. This is not so, most teachers have been press-ganged into it. Dark hooded figures from the Education Department creep around the country. If they find someone just standing around leaning against a wall, looking into a shop window, or waiting to cross a road, then they throw a sack over their head, bundle them into the back of a van, and take them off to be a teacher. This is why most teachers have a dazed look, it is because they are still wondering how they ended up in the job.

Teacher training

Teacher training comes in separate parts:

- Lion-taming. Trainee teachers are given a chair and a whip and put into a cage with thirty hungry lions. If they are still alive when the cage door is opened twenty minutes later, then they have passed the first test.

- Shouting. All teachers are trained to shout when talking, even if the person they are talking to is only three centimetres away. You can always spot a teacher, even off-duty, because if you go up to them in the street and ask them what the time is, they will bellow back at you

'THE TIME IS TEN PAST THREE!!!!' (or whatever the time is) so loudly that your eardrums will fall out and your hair will shrink.

- Eye transplants. All teachers have an additional pair of eyes transplanted into the back of their head. This is so that they can keep watching the class even while they are writing on the blackboard.

- Pens. All teachers are issued with a special pen that can write certain phrases all on its own. These phrases include:

> Writing untidy
> See me
> I expected better work from you than this
> Speling neads improoving

Teachers' pay

Teachers are paid by brain-weight. At the start of a school year all the pupils' heads are weighed and their total weight worked out. The teacher then gets paid only if that total weight increases. In theory this would only happen if the pupils' brains get bigger and heavier, but in practice many teachers cheat by encouraging their pupils to wear cast iron ear-rings and wigs made of concrete.

How teachers dress

Untidy – *Looking as if they have put their clothes on with a shovel*

Sporty – *Wearing huge plimsolls and weighed down by stopwatches and clipboards*

Mad scientist –
Wearing a laboratory coat that used to be white but now has been stained by every known chemical

Forgetful

Maths

Maths is all about numbers and includes multiplication, addition, subtraction and divisions (first division, second division, etc).

It also includes theorems for finding out the sizes of angles and things called logarithms.

Logarithm This is the musical beat played to lumberjacks to help them cut down trees faster.

Trigonometry This is another word for learning to be 'quick on the draw' in the old Wild West.

How to work out the size of an angle Measure him or her from the tip of one wing to the tip of the other wing. (To get hold of an angle, they are usually found in Heaven sitting on clouds playing harps).

Pie This is a mathematical term that is something to do with being circular (or round). If a pie is round it is called a pie. If it is square or oblong it is not a pie, it is just a stew with pastry on it.

English language

Really this should just be about words that we all use anyway and so it should be the easiest subject of the lot and everyone should get A-pluses in it. Unfortunately, teachers have made it harder by introducing things like spelling, commas, apostrophes and verbs.

Spelling English spelling makes no sense at all. For example, look at words ending in '-ough':

'cough' is pronounced 'koff'
'through' is pronounced 'threw'
'rough' is pronounced 'ruff'
'bough' is pronounced 'bow'.

So:

'The rough boy's cough made the bough fall and hit a cow'

could (if you got them all wrong) be read as:-

'The row boy's cue made the buff fall and hit a cough.'

But if you read it that way your English teacher would go mad and start eating your exercise book.

Apostrophe This never existed before Herbert McClock invented the wonky typewriter in 1743. The result was that all his commas kept being typed up in the air instead of on the line. People thought he must know something that they didn't, so they all began sticking commas up in the air. They are no use at all.

Comprehension This means: 'Have you understood what you have just read?' The usual answer is No.

English literature

English Literature means poetry and novels and stuff. Most English Literature is actually not written by English people at all but by Scots and Irish and Welsh and Americans, so it's all really a bit of fraud. However, here are some important books and poems that you should know if you want to be brilliant in English Literature:

● WILLIAM SHAKESPEARE. He wrote the famous poem that goes:

> De dum de dum de dum de dum
> De dum de something dum
> De dum de dum de dum de dum
> And so Alas poor Yorick!

- WUTHERING HEIGHTS by Charles Dickens. A great book in which at the end you find a recipe for making ice cream out of strawberries.

- TREASURE ISLAND by Esmerelda Higginbottom. In which Jim Lad's parrot has a wooden leg, dies from it and becomes a Polygon.

Humanities

This means things that human beings do, such as History (What They Did): Geography (Where They Did It); and Sociology (Why They Did It).

History

History is about what happened since the world began. Because of this it is full of Important Dates and Famous People, all of which you have to remember. These include:

Important dates

- 0 BC – world begins.
- BC – world full of dinosaurs, fossils and Romans.
- 0 AD – calendar invented
- 1066 – someone called Norman turns up in History
- 1600 and something: Columbus discovers America, Australia, India and the ball-point pen which he lost two years earlier.

Famous people

- Ghenghis Khan't
- Mark O'Polo
- Ben Dover
- Mahatma Coat
- Walter Wall Carpets
- Teresa Green
- Lucy Lastic
- King Kong

Geography

This is an important subject because with Geography you can work out where you are on the World. Do you know where you are? You do! Good! That is thanks to Geography!

Sociology

This is the Science of studying society. To do this go out into the street and take a look at it as it goes past.

Chemistry

Chemistry is great because you get to mix different chemicals together and blow the school up.

All chemicals have enormous long names which, because no-one can either pronounce them or spell them properly, have been shortened to chemical symbols.

Here are a few well-known chemical symbols and the chemicals to which they refer:

- H20 – a small motorway running parallel to the M20.
- Ox – a large hairy chemical with long horns that goes 'Mooo!'
- pH – I pHorget what this one is.

Biology

Biology is about how we (and plants) are made. *This is a picture of William Shakespeare showing his skeleton, brain, stomach, liver, and kidneys.*

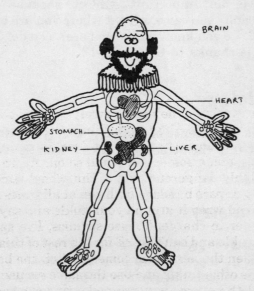

This is called The Complete Works of William Shakespeare.

This is a picture of the skeleton of a leaf to show you the difference between William Shakespeare and a plant.

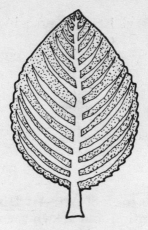

PE

This consists of doing extremely dangerous things with your body in a gym, things like climbing up ropes, bouncing on trampolines, jumping over boxes, doing somersaults and so on. All in all it's a highly dangerous part of the school timetable. Keep a spare bandage with you at all times so that you can wrap it around your ankle and say to the teacher in charge, 'Please sir/miss, I've sprained my ankle and can't do PE for the rest of this term.'

When the next term comes, switch the bandage to the other ankle and use the same excuse. If you have three legs, you can make this excuse last a whole school year. If you haven't, wrap the bandage around your arm and try the 'bad arm' dodge when the third term comes along. However, you're less safe trying this one on because the PE teacher can always tell you to go for a five mile walk instead of doing PE.

Art

There are two sorts of Art: Art History and Art Practical (painting and drawing and things).

Art History

Art began with cavemen painting on the walls of their caves. They did this because they couldn't get hold of any wallpaper. They couldn't get hold of any wallpaper because it hadn't been invented yet. Some useful famous artists to impress the art teacher with are:

● MICHELANGELO & LEONARDO DA VINCI. These were a pair of house decorators and they painted lots of ceilings. They did this because people thought they weren't good enough to paint on walls. One of the most famous ceilings they painted was in a place called the

Cistern Chapel. As you can tell by the name, it was actually the ceiling of the Chapel's toilet and it was above the cistern.

- CONSTABLE. As his name suggests, he was a part-time policeman and painter. Not only did he paint his own pictures but he also framed them, as well as framing many petty crooks. He was said to paint with conviction. After many years of painting he received the ultimate accolade when he was promoted to Sergeant.

41

- VAN GOGH. He came from the famous Van family, as did Minnie Van, the inventor of the small lorry. He was known for cutting off his ear when he was unhappy with a painting. He only ever did two paintings because after the second, he'd run out of ears.

- PICASSO. Known as 'Blockhead' by his friends. Many people thought this referred to his style of painting but actually it was because he was an idiot.

Art Practical

Guide lines to drawing

- For best results, use a pencil with the pointed end downwards.

Crafts

Crafts include things like pottery, metalwork, woodwork, basketmaking, making a nuclear bomb out of a washing up liquid container, etc.

My own favourite craft is Making A Printing Block From An Apple or Other Food. Here's how to do it:

Take an apple. Eat a bit of it. Eat another bit. Eat another bit. Eat another bit. When you have eaten enough of it, take the piece that is left and press it on to an ink pad. Then press it on to a sheet of paper.

Now try it with a bag of chips.

Language

This should mean any language that isn't English, but usually in school it just means French or German. Sometimes it also means Latin.

French

French is the language they speak in France. To speak it properly you need to wear a beret on your head and wave your arms frantically.

Here are a few everyday French expressions with their translations:

- a la carte – my car has got a puncture.

- cordon bleu – You villain, you have stolen my carrot!

- Coup de grace – cut the grass.

- bon voyage – is that your own nose?

- faux pas – footpath reserved for foxes.

- Oui oui – where is the toilet?

- repondez s'il vous plait – where did you have your hair done?

German

German is a really difficult language to learn because it is so full of grammar and suffers heavily from something called Gender. Gender means whether a word is masculine, feminine, neuter, plural, or unpronounceable. For example in German the word 'the' can be one of this lot:

der die das don dun dib dob din

Also, all nouns in German are required by law to have at least 26 letters in them. This is often achieved by putting lots of little nouns together into one long one. This therefore makes it very difficult to say a German noun without running out of breath. Here are some examples of German nouns and their meanings in English:

Die Haushaltabswascheneinkaufen (trans: the washing up)

Eine Kopfschmerzengrippehasschmerzen (trans: a cold)

Ein Entzweizerrissenbeschmutztessenessenessen (trans: a snack).

Latin

This was the language spoken by dead Romans. Here are some useful everyday Latin phrases in case you should ever bump into a dead Roman and need to make conversation.

- Status quo – What do you think of old heavy metal bands?

- ad infinitum – buy a new calculator.

- hic hoc – that cucumber sandwich has given me hiccups.

- in toto – watch out, the Lone Ranger's coming!

- amor omnia vincit – Vincent's armour is rusty.

- non compos mentis – don't lie on the compost heap.

HOW TO PASS EXAMS

There are three ways to pass exams:

1. Be a genius
2. Work very hard and memorize every fact in the universe
3. Cheat

I will pass over the first two methods and move straight to number 3.

Cheating, and how to do it

The bandage trick

Write all the facts you need to know on a bandage and wrap it around your leg or arm or your head. You can also write the facts you need inside a sticking plaster and stick it somewhere about your body (e.g. your hand). You can also try writing answers on the inside of an eyepatch. In fact, if you com-

pletely encase yourself in bandages, sticking plasters and eye patches, etc, you can walk into an exam room carrying every bit of information from the Encylopedia Britannica. However, you will have two problems with this method:

1. The examiner will be suspicious of you when you hobble in looking like an Egyptian mummy on the loose. Tell him or her that you have just suffered a terrible accident, but one that wasn't bad enough to prevent you from taking the exam (e.g. You fractured an eyelash but your doctor is taking no chances).

2. When you start taking the bandages and plasters off to get at the answers, the examiner will notice. Say you feel better suddenly.

The 'Answers already in place' trick

Before the exam starts, write out all the facts you will need on sheets of paper and stick them with sticky tape underneath one of the desks in the exam room.

There is only one problem with this method: you might end up sitting at another desk that doesn't have any answers. If this happens point out to the examiner the desk with the hidden answers and say 'That person there is cheating. Can I have their marks for being honest?'

The 'Sitting next to a brainy person' trick

This is fine in theory, but there are a few problems in practice:

1. The desks are placed too far apart to see what the brainy person is writing.

2. Brainy people write too fast to keep up with.

The way to deal with these problems is:

1. Wear very strong glasses or a pair of binoculars, a telescope, or (if sitting behind a brainbox) a periscope. To make absolutely sure, wear all of them.

2. Every now and then lean over and bash the arm the brainy person is writing with. This will slow them down.

The 'Having the answers already written' trick

Write out the answers to every question that is likely to come up in the exam and smuggle them into the exam room with you. This will mean smuggling in about ten thousand pages of writing, but if you stuff them up your sleeves and under your jumper, perhaps the examiner will just think you're very fat.

Multiple choice exam papers

These are the new style exams being used more and more to help people who can't read and can't write to pass an exam. As you probably know, it goes something like this:

MATHS: 2 plus 2 is:

a) 3 b) 4 c) 5.897 d) a banana

You then have to poke the point of your pencil through the answer which you think is correct.

The easiest way to do multiple choice exams

Simple. Take your pencil and mark every (c) all the way down a whole section. With the next section mark every (a) throughout the whole section. Then the next section mark every (b); then the section after that mark every (d). This way the examiners won't get suspicious.

This system works on the idea that some of the answers you have marked *must* be correct, certainly at least 1 in 4, which will give you a fairly respectable mark of 25%.

This system is obviously for those people who Do Not Have A Clue about a subject. If you do Have A Clue, try guessing. I bet you still won't get more marks than if you'd used MY system, so Yah Boo Sucks.

The general knowledge perfect answer paper

Every now and then you'll get an exam called General Knowledge. This is about all the knowledge in the whole universe, and as an aid to all school students, I have compiled the following Perfect Answer Paper. It works on the same basic random principle as the 'Multiple-Choice Exam Answering' method. The only difference is that this time you will actually have to read the question so that you can choose the answer that looks vaguely as if it will fit the question.

The general knowledge perfect answer paper

1. True
2. False
3. Perhaps
4. 16
5. 1066
6. 25%
7. Inside half an apple
8. Plastic underwear
9. The Equator
10. The hump-backed whale
11. Two pimples
12. £5.37
13. A penguin with a bowler hat on
14. No
15. Yes
16. The rear end of a horse
17. Dandruff
18. Balls
19. The London A-D telephone directory
20. Knitting
21. Queen Elizabeth I's false teeth
22. Sideways
23. Genghis Khan
24. 25 centimetres
25. Because heat rises
26. Once only
27. You can pat a cow but you can't pat a cow pat
28. 1986
29. Abraham Lincoln's ear
30. Backwards.

Games at school are not what you'd hope they'd be, such as Snakes and Ladders, or Draughts, or seeing who can balance a hard-boiled egg on their nose the longest. Games at school are team games such as football, netball, hockey or cricket.

Team games are immensely dangerous activities for two reasons: a) the other team; b) the other members of your own team.

The other team

These are usually super-fit super-agile super-skilled people built like brick walls on legs. Their physical co-ordination and teamwork are superb and they

usually slaughter your team by 4 million goals to nil, or 27,000 runs to none.

Your team

Your team haven't got a brain between them and couldn't get a ball into a goal if it was the size of the Grand Canyon. However, every time they lose they look round for someone in the team to blame, and that person is nearly always YOU. This means that you spend the next few hours after the game hiding in the toilets or up a tree while your team roam around armed with bits of goalpost looking for you.

How to get out of games

An illness or some sort of injury is the obvious first choice here.

Illnesses

It obviously has to be a short illness, one that you catch as you are about to get changed for games, and from which you miraculously recover as the game ends. Illnesses like these are in short supply. The only one that really fits the bill is food poisoning, and the trouble is that if you fall over with food poisoning every time you are about to get changed for games, one of two things will happen:

a. people will get suspicious

b. Your school cook will be arrested by the Food Police from some Ministry and your school kitchen will be closed down (which may not be a bad thing).

You could try sneezing a lot and saying 'Please Sir/Miss, I think I've got flu.' Unfortunately most teachers are so hard-hearted they couldn't care less if you've got bubonic plague. They just say 'Get out on that field. The fresh air will do you good.' However, here is a list of illnesses which you can try to persuade your teacher you are suffering from:

- rheumatism
- typhoid
- a common cold
- malaria
- swamp fever
- a swollen head
- tennis elbow
- housemaid's knee
- Yeti's toenails
- Frankenstein's foot
- lumbago

Injuries

These are another good way to get out of games. They are better than illnesses because it makes you look as if you *have been* keen *in the past*. The best sort is an 'injury' before games. For this, all you need to do is bandage some part of your anatomy that is vital to the game (e.g. your foot if it's football), and then hobble, limp or crawl up to your teacher and say 'I'm afraid I'm injured.'

The drawback here is that this only works on two occasions at the most, as even the most idiotic teacher will get suspicious if you keep injuring the same limb seven or eight weeks on the trot. (You could always have it amputated but that's a bit desperate.)

You could try injuring a different limb each week, but after a while news of all these continuous injuries will get on to your school report and when you leave school no employer will want to give you a job because everyone will think you are ultra-prone to accidents.

This leaves us with the injury *during* Games. This is simple to achieve. As soon as the game starts, you rush over to the biggest person on the other team, crash into them, then fall on the ground clutching your leg and moaning with pain.

One important point to remember: make sure the way you are injured fits the game. The above technique is fine for games like football, hockey, netball, basketball, but it won't work if the game is cricket. Can you honestly imagine any batsman suddenly rushing up to the nearest fielder, crashing into him and falling over? And can you honestly see people believing it was an accident?

Good injuries

Here is a list of injuries, which you can use to persuade your teacher to let you off.

- a ruptured eyelash
- a twisted ear-lobe
- a squashed nostril
- a loose tooth
- a fractured hair

(Don't try these unless your teacher is pretty stupid.)

SPORTS DAYS

Sports Days are awful, unless you are one of your school's star athletes. As star athletes are only about 0.5% of the school population, the chances are that you are one of the remaining 99.5% who get a stitch halfway through any race, or tread on their laces and fall over right in front of the largest part of the crowd.

Among the worst things about Sports Day (actually there are hundreds of worst things about it) are:

1. You can't get out of it because everyone is expected to take part, even if they've got three legs and can't run properly.

2. Your parents insist on turning up 'to support you'. This means that not only do you suffer the public shame of coming last about 100 kilometres behind everyone else, but you also end up with terrible guilt because your parents have taken the day off work to see it happen.

So, to stop you having to live a life of Public Shame and Guilt, here is how you can WIN ON SPORTS DAY.

Races

- Tie your competitors' shoelaces together.

- Remove your competitors' shoelaces.

- Remove the elastic from the waist of their shorts.

- If the start uses running blocks, spread glue on them so that their shoes stick to the blocks.

- Pour oil on your competitors' lanes so that they slip over.

- Arrange for someone to set a fierce dog on your competitors before your race. The dog will chase them and they will be too worn out to run fast.

- Fill your competitors up with drinks.

- Offer the other competitors a sweet before the race, but make sure it has some extra ingredient in it that makes them feel sick.

High jump and long jump

- Put the other competitors off by saying something off-putting as they run to attempt their jump:

  'You've just trod in some dog mess'
  'Your shorts are falling down'
  'Your mother's just fallen over'

- As you walk past, tread on your competitors' feet.

- Before the event, put the other competitors off by telling them how someone was seriously injured while taking part in a similar event, (e.g. 'They fell awkwardly and damaged their knee, and now they can't walk. Apparently it happens to 73% of people who go in for the high jump (or long jump).'

- Tell the Judges that the other competitors are cheating and should be disqualified,

  'Number 7 has got springs in his /her shoes.'
  'His/her friend is working the bar and keeps lowering it as he/she goes over.'

Sack race

Before the race starts put any of the following in your competitors' sacks:-

- rats
- mice
- snakes
- glue
- bricks
- manure

Egg and spoon race

- Stick your egg to your spoon with glue

Putting the shot or throwing the weight

- Switch your competitors' weight for one that is extra, extra heavy so that they can barely lift it, let alone throw it.

- As they lift their arm to throw the weight, use a pea-shooter to fire a small object that will hit them in the armpit. They will drop the weight immediately.

School trips come in two different types:

1. Day trips, where you get taken to a museum, a zoo, or a theatre for the afternoon performance of a play by Shakespeare or someone.

2. School holidays lasting about a week. These holidays come in three sorts:

   a) holidays abroad

   b) a week walking around a town looking at ancient buildings, museums, etc.

   c) a week camping.

Day trips

Museums

The one great thing about really old museums is their echo. You can shout 'Hello!' and it comes back 'Helloooooooooooooo!' as if you were in a cave. Unfortunately you then get thrown out by the attendants and have to listen to your teacher moaning at you all the way back to school.

The thing that no-one ever explains properly is why so many things in museums are broken. How did this happen? Did the delivery people drop the objects when they were delivering them? Did the cleaners knock them over and break them? And if this is so why don't they replace them with new ones?

Zoos

The big danger when visiting a zoo is that you and the rest of your school party will not be allowed out again. This is because so many human beings resemble animals. Suspicious Zoo attendants have been claiming that some people leaving are actually animals dressed up making a bid for freedom. You can see what they mean when you compare some teachers (and pupils) with their animal look-alikes:

Theatre trips

The unfair thing about theatre trips is that you are not allowed to make any noise at all. If you can't hear what the actors are saying because they are mumbling and you dare to ask the person next to you what's going on — what happens? Do they stop the play and explain to you what you've missed, like any decent company of actors should? Do they go back a few pages and do it again so that you can catch up? No they don't, they throw you out in the street. This is most unfair and there ought to be a law against it.

A typical visit to a performance of a play by Shakespeare goes like this:

You are all turfed off the coach and lined up outside the theatre like a bunch of prisoners about to be deported. Then the English teacher in charge strides up and down the pavement giving you your instructions.

'Right!' bellows the teacher. 'You are going to see this brilliant play by William Shakespeare called "Twelfth Night". This is a very funny play indeed and is known as one of Shakespeare's greatest comedies. If I catch anyone laughing during the performance they will be in terrible trouble.'

Then the teachers frisk everyone and remove all objects such as crisps, bubblegum, elastic bands, machine guns, shoelaces, and any other thing which they consider might make a noise or cause a disturbance while you are in the theatre.

Then you all file into the theatre, and it takes about ten hours to get everyone seated. This is because the teacher in charge keeps moving children about because all teachers are afraid to allow friends to sit together in case they talk to each other. This means that everyone is placed next to someone they don't like, so they start fighting and arguing instead. When this happens everyone is moved about again. As I said, this all takes about ten hours, by which time the actors come out and begin to complain because they want to get on with the play.

'Right!' says the teacher again. 'Sit down and be quiet everyone. You are about to see a brilliant play called . . . (blah, blah, blah)'

At which point someone else in the theatre gets fed up with your teacher and chucks a brick at him or her, which knocks your teacher into the nearest seat, and the play gets under way.

A typical Shakespeare play

Enter a gravedigger.

GRAVEDIGGER: What ho, alas alack. Tis I, a poor gravedigger. I' faith, I am in reality a Prince who was swapped at birth with the son of a Boot and Shoe Mender. What ho.

Exits stage left to dig grave with shovel (but finds it difficult because stage is made of wood).
Enter a Fool

FOOL: I am a Fool.

To prove it he pours custard down his trousers.
Enter King.

KING: What ho, Fool!
FOOL: What ho!
KING: What doest thou here?

FOOL: I doest whatsoever thou doest when thou doest what I dost do when I dost do what thou doest.
KING: Bravely spoken! (*looks off stage*) What ho, for here comes a lowly gravedigger!

Enter gravedigger, bearing shovel.

KING: What ho!
FOOL: What ho!

The gravedigger, fed up with all this what-hoing, bashes them both over the head with his shovel.

GRAVEDIGGER: Now I am once more the rightful King and yea, I shall find my two long-lost sisters and my cat Ginger. What ho.

Exit gravedigger. End of play.

In real time all of this takes about four hours, by which time you have all fallen asleep and missed the bit at the end where the detective comes on and announces that the butler did it.

School holidays

Holidays abroad

Generally speaking these would be great if it weren't for the fact that you are expected to fill in work sheets about the place where you are staying.

A guide to points of interest on school trips abroad (Places to watch out for)

Paris (France)

1. The Eiffel Tower. Constructed as a model for the ice-cream cone by Hector Eiffel in 1792. It should have been built the other way up (the pointed bit on the ground), but it kept falling over and bashing passing Parisians on the head.

2. Cathedral of Notre Dame. Named after the famous pantomime dame, Widow Twankey.

3. The River Seine. (Pronounced 'Sane'). Built in 1555 by Pierre le Twit, a complete madman who couldn't build straight rivers. Because of that, this river bent all the way through Paris. When people complained and accused him of being bonkers, Pierre replied 'Non, je suis sane!' ('No, I am sane!') The people thought he was saying 'The river is sane', which is how it got its name.

Switzerland

Snow (lots of it), skiers and chocolate.

Germany

All the towns in Germany are named after fast foods (e.g. hamburger = Hamburg; frankfurter = Frankfurt; fish and chips = Munchen. So called because you munch fish and chips.)

River Rhine This river got its name from the wet stuff that fell on it and caused it to be a river – i.e. 'rain'. Originally it was called the River Rain, but very few Germans could pronounce it properly.

Italy

1. **The Leaning Tower of Pizza.** As is obvious from its name, this tower was originally an enormous pizza that was baked standing on one end. It started to fall over, but turned stale just as it started to lean.

2. **Rome.** This is where the Pope lives. If you're passing his house, knock on the front door and pop in for a cup of tea. Say that Mrs Willis sent you.

A week walking around an ancient town

The educational idea behind this is that children will look at all these old buildings and castles and 'experience' how people used to live in 'Olden Tymes'. In fact this is nonsense because most of these old buildings have been knocked down and turned into car parks and hamburger or pizza places. After a week spent walking around one of these towns, most schoolchildren come away with the idea that the Romans (or Saxons):

NUMBER XVII

- played bingo
- ate hamburgers, pizzas, kebabs, etc
- wrote slogans in support of football teams on walls
- went shopping in supermarkets
- parked their chariots in multi-storey car parks
- all worked in large office blocks

But then, maybe they did.

Camping

Avoid this like the plague.

Camping means living in a tent and having to wash in cold water. It means that every known form of insect turns up in swarms to attack you. The other major problems with camping are:

- When it rains the camp turns into a field of mud about three metres deep and people disappear and are never seen again.

- The tent poles collapse.

- The zip of your tent sticks with the tent flap open on the first night, and you slowly freeze to death over the next six nights.

- You have to eat out in the open and either:
  a) you have a hot dinner which goes stone cold within seconds in the open air

  OR

  b) you have salad and a strong wind turns up and blows it off your plate

- There is no TV or video.

- In fact there is no entertainment of any kind, all there is to see is scenery. See one tree and one bush and you've seen it all.

- On at least one evening you will be ordered to sit around the camp fire and sing songs. To get out of this:
  a) say that you've got laryngitis
  b) pour water on the campfire earlier in the day
  c) sing a rude song and get sent to your tent.

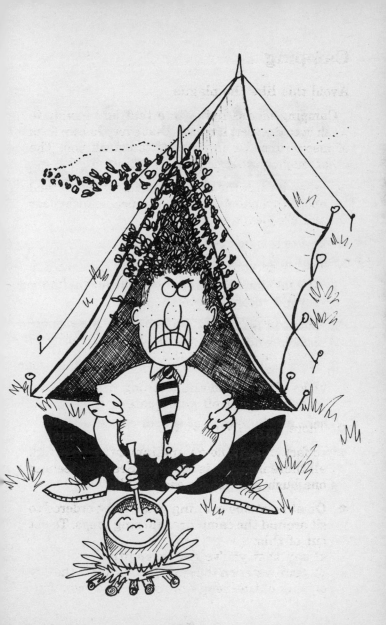

SCHOOL MEALS

School meals come in three sorts

1. Old-fashioned, where everything is boiled beyond recognition.

2. Modern fast-food, where everything is pre-cooked and plastic.

3. No school meals at all but you have to take your own sandwiches.

There are two sorts of school cooks:

1. Great cooks who believe in healthy food that tastes great.

2. Old-fashioned cooks.

76

Because 'Great Cooks' are a rarity and not often encountered in schools (they make up about 1% of school cooks), I shall concentrate instead on the old-fashioned variety (the remaining 99%).

How an old-fashioned cook cooks

Cabbages and greens These are boiled until all the colour has disappeared from them. They are then painted green using household paint.

Potatoes, boiled These are either so lightly boiled that you break your knife on them if you try to cut them; or boiled so long that they evaporate as you poke them with a fork.

Potatoes, mashed This looks like wallpaper paste both in texture and taste. There is in fact only one way to tell the difference between school mashed potatoes and wallpaper paste, and that is to stick rolls of wallpaper up with it. If the paper falls off when it dries, it was mashed potato.

Potatoes, chips These are also known as French Fries. They aren't made from real potatoes. Instead they are made out of the infamous wallpaper paste (see 'mashed' above) turned into spaghetti. Thin spaghetti remains just that. The spaghetti that comes out of the machine a bit too fat is chopped into short bits and becomes chips.

Carrots The same as for 'Cabbages and greens', but they are painted orange instead of green.

Sausages Have you ever wondered what's inside a sausage? Have you ever noticed how a sausage keeps rolling off your plate when you try to poke it with a fork? Well, here's a clue, it's not rolling, it's trying to escape!

Toad-in-the-hole This is too disgusting to describe here. The name alone is enough to tell you what it is. Have the salad instead.

Meat pies See 'Sausages', and ask yourself, have any of the teachers in your school gone missing lately? How soon after they went missing did you have a meat pie?

Wholefoods This means stuff that is organically grown and you get the whole goodness of the food without it being peeled, squeezed, processed and coloured and having loads of chemicals and E numbers added to it. However, old-fashioned school cooks have never understood wholefoods, they think that 'wholefood cooking' means they cook the whole of it. If you ask an old-fashioned school cook to prepare wholefood they will simply take the whole thing to be cooked (e.g. a potato, a fish, a cabbage, a cow, a horse, etc) and boil it in one piece in an enormous saucepan until it tastes like a boiled wellington boot.

The ten most popular school meals

1. Chips
2. Chips
3. Chips
4. Chips
5. Chips
6. Chips
7. Chips
8. Chips
9. Chips
10. Chips

SCHOOL BUILDINGS

School buildings are either generally very old, in which case the ceiling falls down and doors come off their hinges the moment you walk into a classroom or they are so new that they are made entirely of glass. The glass in these new buildings is always so clear that you can never see the doors, so once your are in you have to spend the next five years trying to find the way back out.

Old buildings

Classrooms

The classrooms in old buildings were obviously built for giants because the ceilings are about fifty metres from the floor. This means that if you should happen to throw something in the air (e.g. a paper aeroplane, an exercise book, the smallest person in your class) and it gets stuck on a light fitting, you'll have to call out the fire brigade to get it down.

Another give-away to the fact that these rooms were built for giants is that the windows are about ten metres high up the walls. This makes it impossible to look out of them unless you bounce up and down on a trampoline.

The school hall

School halls in old buildings are where assemblies and school plays are held. The acoustics are so terrible that no-one can hear a word anyone is saying, and any mass singing sounds as if it is going on inside a wind tunnel.

The school hall is also always collapsing due to the weight on its ancient floor of:

a) the whole school;

b) the whole school plus parents; and

c) the school piano.

New buildings

Classrooms

All classrooms in new buildings are made of glass, just like the rest of the building. This means that everyone can look in and see what the teacher and the class are up to.

As most teachers prefer to spend all lessons fast asleep (after first having written ten questions on the board and said 'Get on with those'), they get very worried that people passing will see them lying on the floor snoring away. For this reason teachers are always urging their pupils to paint pictures which they can stick on the glass walls, to stop people looking in.

If they have a useless class who can't paint pictures, or write stories, or do anything except sit there and look like brick walls with clothes on, then these teachers will cover their glass walls with posters advertising The Destruction of the Rain Forests, etc.

Temporary classrooms (wooden huts)

Whenever a school has too many pupils to fit comfortably into all its rooms, they use two methods to deal with them:

1. They issue the school caretaker with a crowbar, and it is his job to use it to squeeze as many children as possible into a classroom. When this fails and the classroom walls collapse, the second method is used.

2. Temporary wooden huts are brought in. In fact, 'temporary' is not really true in this case as 'temporary' can mean anything from one minute to a million years.

You can always tell which children have their classroom in a hut because in the winter they will be soaking wet from rain coming through the roof, and in summer they will all be fried by the sun cooking them through the glass windows. Temporary huts also always have huge holes in the walls. This is useful for one reason: it allows the children to escape more easily, but it also creates a terrible draught which makes the pupils go stiff up one side, usually the side they keep their brains.

VISITORS TO SCHOOLS

School inspectors, school governors, etc

At some time your school will be visited by someone important in the shape of a school inspector or a school governor, or someone else who has the power to sack all the teachers and wants to see how the school is run. You will know that this is about to happen because all the teachers will start to worry, and they will also make you work harder than you have ever worked before.

Tell-tale signs to watch out for in teachers' behaviour

- Teachers start to go grey with worry overnight.

- They start biting their fingernails.

- They stop going to the pub or the betting office at lunchtime.

- Teachers bring in loads of brilliant paintings, which they sign with the names of children in their class and put on the classroom walls. If the painting already has a signature, they add the name of a child to it: for example: 'Vincent Van Gogh' becomes 'Vincent Van Gogh Johnson'; 'Michelangelo' becomes 'Michael angel O'Grady'.

THE MONA LESLEY

- They tell you what particular lesson they are going to teach you on a particular day, and what questions they will be asking. They also give you all the answers so that you will get every question right on the day of the visit.

- They send all the rotten kids in the class to the school nurse with suspected head lice in the hope that these rotten kids will be banned from coming to school for a week.

- They start marking pupils' work.

- They start to dress smartly, instead of looking as if they've put their clothes on with a shovel.

In fact, a visit by one of these VIPs is a good opportunity for you to make worthwhile deals at school. Just as the car pulls up with the Important Person in it, say to your teacher: 'I promise to behave perfectly throughout this whole day, and be seen to be a brilliant student, providing the following demands are met:

1. Free ice-cream four times a day.

2. No homework.

3. Teacher to set no work at all.

4. If I should do any work at all (i.e. write my name on a piece of paper) I am to get full marks, a Gold Star, an 'A' on my report, and the word 'Excellent' written on my work.

5. I will be allowed to sleep during lessons.

If these demands are not met, I shall have no alternative but to behave badly when the Inspector looks in, and also pretend to be a complete idiot.'

Your teacher will be so desperate to avoid such shame that he or she will agree to all your demands.

However, once the VIP has gone, your teacher will then walk up to you, bash you over the head, snarl 'So you thought you could blackmail me, huh!', and send you down the nearest coal mine to do ten years' hard labour. So maybe it's not such a good idea after all.

Parents

Parents don't often come into school. If they do it is for one of the following reasons:

1. They have come to moan at your teacher about you

2. Your teacher has called them in to moan to them about you

3. It is open day, when teachers and parents get together to talk about your 'progress in school' (or lack of it)

Whichever reason it is, you can be certain of one thing: someone is going to complain about you, and you will be in trouble. To avoid this happening the best thing is to make sure that your parents never make it through the school gates. Here's how:

1. Destroy any notes your teacher gives you to take home.

2. If you suspect your parents are thinking of going to your school, tell them that it is infected with some kind of disease. If they say 'Then why are you still going to school?' reply that it doesn't affect children or members of the teaching profession.

3. Tell your parents that your school buildings have been declared unsafe and may collapse at any moment.

4. Tell your parents that your teacher is a chain-saw wielding maniac who attacks parents.

5. Tell your teacher that your parents are chain-saw wielding maniacs who attack teachers.

If none of these works and your parents do make it to your school, here are a few tips.

1. Put something in your teacher's cup of coffee that makes him or her lose their voice.

2. If it is an Open Day visit to 'look at your work', put your name on the covers of the exercise books of the most brilliant person in your class.

Sports and TV stars and other celebrities

Sooner or later a famous sports star or a TV or film star will come to visit your school. When that happens everyone at your school will want to meet them and get their autograph and shake their hand. The question is: how do you make sure that YOU are one of the children who get to meet them? This is how to do it.

1. Attract their attention by carrying a huge banner saying 'Come and talk to me or I'll bash your face in!'

2. Attract their sympathy by wearing a bandage around your head, or over your face, or encasing your leg in plaster of paris. If you really want to make absolutely sure that they stop and say 'Hello' to you, then do the whole lot: bandage your head, arms, legs, body, AND turn up at school on that day in a wheelchair.

3. Write a letter to the star concerned a week or so before they arrive at your school saying the following:

   'Dear (whatever the name of the star is), I am the mother of (write your name here), who has been a fan of yours for many many years, and he/she was delighted when the news was announced that you will be visiting his/her school on (whatever the date of the visit is).

   My son /daughter has been seriously ill for some time with (bronchitis/mumps/

measles/bubonic plague, etc), but will be getting out of his/her hospital bed on that special day and will be going to school especially just to see you. Please make a very ill child very happy by stopping to say hello to him /her. I hope you can do this as if you don't it is quite likely the disappointment of not talking to you will cause my child to suffer a relapse and he/she will have to go back into hospital for the next ten years to recover.

Yours sincerely,

etc etc etc'

THE NATIVITY PLAY

Once a year, just before Christmas, most schools engage in a ritual called the school Nativity Play, where parents are dragged in off the streets and forced to sit and watch their offspring re-enact the events leading up to the birth of Jesus in Bethlehem in the Year Nought. This in itself is a very commendable thing, but what I want to know is: why do certain children always only get to play a sheep while all the others get to be Wise Men and Kings?

How to play a sheep in the Nativity Play

Find a carpet. Kneel down on all fours and get someone to put the carpet over you. You are now a sheep. That is about all there is to it. You can try going 'Baa' now and then, just in case the

Mooo!

audience think you are a cow or a horse. However, if you do this, be warned — the teacher in charge may get annoyed with you and say that you are ruining the production. If this happens there is a good chance that you will not even be allowed to be a sheep but will end up looking after the Three Kings' presents in the classroom behind the hall that is acting as the dressing room. This means that no-one will see you and your parents will be most disappointed.

If this does happen to you, then here is a good way to get your own back: open up the box that is supposed to contain myrrh and fill it with sneezing powder. When the King presents this box to Mary and Joseph and they open it, they will start sneezing so hard they will fall off the stage.

Other important roles in the Nativity Play and how to play them

A Roman soldier

For this you get to dress up in cardboard covered in silver paper. (Or was that the time I played a Dalek in an assembly? Oh no, now I remember! I accidentally put on the wrong costume just before going on, and ended up coming on stage as a Dalek in ancient Bethlehem. However, I got out of what could have been a nasty situation by some nifty thinking. I pointed my finger at Joseph, croaked 'Exterminate!' and then wobbled offstage, where Miss Pankhurst (who was in charge of the play) bashed me on the head.)

A shepherd

This is not too difficult, all you have to do is put on some old rags and sit by some red tinsel paper watching your flocks. The first time I was given this role to play I misheard the teacher and thought she said 'Sit by the fire washing your socks', so I came on stage with a bowl of soapy water. Unfortunately, I tripped over my robe and soaked two of the sheep, who got up and kicked me.

A wise man

It is noticeable that only the school idiots are chosen to play Wise Men, children who can't even pick their own nose with any degree of success. I think this is most unfair and that Certain Other People should have a go.

A king

This is all right, but it has one major problem: the crown. The crown you will be given is certain to be the wrong size. It will either be too big or too small. If it is too small it will keep sliding off your head, so you will have to spend the whole nativity play holding it on your head with one hand. This only leaves you with one hand free to hold the Gift (Gold, Frankincense, Myrrh, etc). This is nearly impossible as these gifts are always in huge great boxes the size of Long John Silver's treasure chest. You could always try holding the crown in place with an elastic band, but these tend to hurt your ears.

On the other hand, if the crown is too big it will slide off your head and fall over your eyes, completely blindfolding you. You will then stumble straight into the stable, trip over the crib, and bring the whole lot down. Better to play a sheep.

The star

This is not a good part to play if you don't like heights, as you have to stand on a ladder at the side of the stage. I only played it once and I got giddy and fell off and landed on Mrs Thrupston who was playing the piano. It took the school caretaker three hours to untangle her from the strings inside the piano.

An angel

This is quite a good part because you actually get to speak. You have to turn up while the shepherds are washing their socks and say 'Lo, I bring you good tidings!' The trouble is you are then supposed to tell the shepherds what the good tidings are, but you get so overcome by all the attention being on you at long last that you forget what the Good Tidings are and you replace them with something like: 'Arsenal won at home to Liverpool'. You will then leave the stage and be bashed over the head by Miss Pankhurst (or whoever is in charge of your Nativity Play).

Joseph and Mary

These are great parts. You will not get them, they go to the ones the teacher likes best. This is all very unfair and is the reason why people in the audience often comment on the fact that the sheep keep bashing the legs of Mary and Joseph when they're in the stable.

The starring role in this whole production is obviously that of JESUS, but no-one gets to play that. Instead the part is usually played by a doll. You could try standing under a lift as it comes down so that you end up 30 centimetres high, but as you will also then be about ten metres wide they still won't be able to fit you into the crib, so it doesn't really work.

SCHOOL REPORTS

STEWART'S
BAD BOY
DOESN'T
WORK
FOR CLASS

School reports are immensely dangerous things. This is because most school reports are terrible and full of lies about you (e.g. that you are not very clever and that your behaviour is awful. In my opinion teachers who write such things should be prosecuted under the Trades Descriptions Act or something, because what they put down is only their *opinion* and not a fact.)

Anyway, there you are walking around with this in your pocket and you know that it can cause an explosion in two possible ways:

1. When you hand it in to your parents for them to sign it.

2. If you don't hand it to your parents but just throw it away, and then tell your teacher that you lost it.

Either way, you get into trouble.

History of the school report

In the old days teachers used just to write anything down in school reports, no matter how scandalous or libellous it was. This was because hardly anybody could read so it was unlikely that a child's parent would come rushing up to the school, bash the teacher in the nose and say 'How dare you say such things about my child!'

So a typical Old Tyme school report would read something like this:

ENGLISH: Has ye hedde of ye turnippe.

MATHS: This child is ye idiotte and cannot even count how many noses he has, let alone ye fingers of ye eache hand.

BEHAVIOUR: This childe should be boiled in oil.

PARENT TO SIGN. (Put 'X' here). . . . .

However, as adults started to read and understood what was being said about their child, they began to get annoyed. Sometimes this annoyance took the form of bashing the teacher with an axe or a suit of armour or something.

To stop this happening to them, teachers began to be more careful when writing out school reports. They still said the same terrible things, but they said them in ways that they hoped parents wouldn't see through:

e.g. 'An interesting child' meant 'This child should be boiled in oil.'

All was quiet for a few centuries, but then parents began to understand what teachers were up to, and as soon as they learnt what this Doublespeak actually meant, they went back to going to the school and bashing teachers again.

Because of this teachers began to fix it so that the school reports laid the blame on the pupils, and ever since then pupils have been at risk!

For that reason the Patent Perfect School Report was invented. All you have to do when you get your school report is to throw it away and replace it with this, and your parents will shower you with love and kisses and presents and put you up for the Nobel Prize for being a genius.

The Patent Perfect School Report

English language: This child can spell every word ever invented, including 'antidisestablishmentarianism' and 'supercalafragilistithingy'.

English literature: This child has written twenty-seven plays this term, any of which is as good as any play by William Shakespeare, Enid Blyton and Donald Duck all rolled into one. Also, if Wordsworth ever reads one of this pupil's poems he will pack up poetry writing as a dead loss and go back to sweeping chimneys.

Maths: Dr Frank Einstein telephoned this school yesterday desperate to solve a mathematical problem and this child was the only one who could help him. It is a privilege to be in the same room as this child's brain.

Religious knowledge: This child has memorized the Bible, the Koran, the Torah, and the Complete Book of Knitting Patterns. He/she has also organized three International Conferences on Religious Unity while at the same time playing 'Mull of Kintyre' on the mouth organ.

History: Astonished the whole world of Archaeology by discovering a complete family of dinosaurs still alive and running a Fish and Chip shop in Bognor Regis. For this astounding Historical Discovery he/she has been recommended for the Order of the Knight of the Bombay Duck.

Geography: This child's solo trip around the world on a one-wheeled typewriter created new records in Geographical discovery. A genius.

Games: Despite being picked to play for his/her country in cricket, football, netball, hockey and dominoes in every major international competition this past year, he/she still managed to be the Captain and leading goalscorer in every game played by this school.

PE: This pupil is so fit that we have begged for his/her muscles to be left to the school as mementoes.

Science: Having witnessed this pupil at work, I can now safely state that there are no more discoveries to be made in the world of science. This child has discovered them all!

THE FAVOURITE SCHOOL JOKES

TEACHER: Name four members of the cat family.
BOY: Daddy cat, mummy cat, and two kittens.

MATHS TEACHER: John, give me a sentence with the word 'centimetre' in it.
JOHN: Er, my Granny came to the bus station to visit us, and I was centimetre.

TEACHER: Angela, how can you prove the world is round?
ANGELA: I never said it was.

101

It was the new term and Edward was late for school every day. His teacher had turned a blind eye to it for the first day, but when Edward was late on the third day the teacher demanded an explanation.

'It's the fault of that sign at the end of the road,' said Edward. 'I'd be here on time every day if it wasn't for that.'

'What sign?' demanded his teacher.

'You know,' said Edward. 'The one that says: "School. Go Slow."'

The little girl had just come home after her first day at school.

'What did you learn today?' asked her mother.

'Not enough,' said the girl. 'I've got to go back tomorrow.'

Clare had been messing around in the English class, so her teacher told her to stay in during break and write out a sentence containing not less than forty words. This is the sentence that Clare wrote:

'Mr Jones couldn't find his dog, so he went to his front door, opened it and called out 'Come here, Rover!'

TEACHER: 'Sara, if I had twenty five bananas in my left hand and twenty five bananas in my right hand, what would I have?'
SARA: 'Big hands, sir.'

TEACHER: Marion, I hope I didn't see you copying just then!
MARION: I hope you didn't as well.

TEACHER: Jones, what is the outside of a tree called?
JONES: I don't know, sir.
TEACHER: Bark, boy, bark!
JONES: Woof woof!

TEACHER: How old do you think I am?

BOY: Forty, sir.

TEACHER: Good heavens, that's exactly right! How did you work that out?

BOY: Well my brother's twenty, and you're twice as potty as he is.

TEACHER: Wayne, spell 'wrong'.

WAYNE: R – O – N – G.

TEACHER: That's wrong.

WAYNE: Well that's what you asked for.

TEACHER: Janet, I told you to write this passage out twenty times because your handwriting is so bad, and you've only written it out ten times. Why?

JANET: My arithmetic is bad as well, sir.

TEACHER: Smith, why is it that you can't answer any of the questions I ask you?

SMITH: If I could there wouldn't be much point in me coming to school, would there?

TEACHER: Steven, did your father help you with this homework?

STEVEN: No, miss, he did it all on his own.

HISTORY TEACHER: Now, today we are revising the Kings and Queens of England, particularly the Tudors. You will remember that they were Henry VII, Henry VIII, Edward VI, Mary . . . Who can tell me who came after Mary? . . . Well come on, someone must know. Yes, Samantha. Who came after Mary?
SAMANTHA: A little lamb?

TEACHER: Steven, did your father help you with this homework?

STEVEN: No, miss, he did it all on his own.

TEACHER: John, if eggs were £1.20 a dozen, how many would you get for twenty pence?

JOHN: None

TEACHER: None?

JOHN: No, if I'd got twenty pence, I'd buy a bar of chocolate.

TEACHER: Stephanie, do you know where to find an elephant?

STEPHANIE: No, but I reckon they're so big that they don't often get lost.

CHANGING SCHOOLS

This part of the book is especially for those of you who are about to Go Up To Big School. For years now you have been working your way up through the Year Groups in your Junior School (or Lower School or Middle School), and just when you thought you had it made, just when you had become one of the Big Kids in your School and could go around frightening all those kids who were younger than you....you got rumbled, and you are about to be thrown into a High School (or Upper School) and become a Little Kid again! Aaaaarghhhhh!!! Yes, that's how unfair life is.

Of course, you could always try to get out of it by staying in your present school, and to achieve that here are a few excuses you could try:

● I daren't go to the Upper School. The Mafia have put out a contract on me, and the hitman is one of the teachers at that school!

108

- My birth certificate is wrong. I'm actually a year younger than I thought I was!

- I have been so happy at this school, I can't bear to leave it.

- I have discovered that I have a rare illness and the sole antidote is a tiny microbe that lives only in the air in this school.

- Miss/Sir, you are my idol! My heart will break if I can't see you every day!

Frankly, I have to tell you that it is unlikely that any of this will wash. Come the last day of term at your Junior School and your teachers will parcel you up and chuck you in the van with the rest of the unfortunates and send you off to Big School.

Big school

Big school is different from your last school in lots of ways:

1. Instead of staying in one room for all your lessons, you will have to go from classroom to classroom. This is because the teachers in Big School are lazy and unable to walk very far. The teachers in Big School also do not like walking around too much in Big Schools because:
   a) they get lost;
   b) they get mugged by all the millions of huge pupils.

2. As I said in the last section, Big School is so much bigger than Little School that the teachers get lost in it. So do all new pupils. In fact every new pupil gets so lost on their very first day at Big School, what with all the corridors and staircases and loads and loads of different buildings, that it is best as you leave for your first day at Big School to let your parents know that they needn't expect you home for at least four days.

3. Another problem with Big School is that all the other pupils are enormous. In fact some are so big and look so old (i.e. they have moustaches and beards) that it can be difficult to tell them apart from the teachers. This is how to tell the difference: the teachers are the ones who look destitute.

4. Another thing about Big School: the teachers are madder than they are at Little School.

Hints on how not to get lost on your first day at big school

1. Take a map. (In fact Big School will issue you with a map. However, this will not be much use as very few people can understand maps anyway, and they are only really any use if you

110

know where you are on the map, so they are not a lot of use if you are lost.)

2. Take a ball of string. The way this works is as follows: when you walk in through the school doors, tie one end of the ball of string to the door handle and let the string unravel as you walk around all the corridors during the day. At the end of the day, to find your way back to the main entrance, all you have to do is rewind the ball of string.

There is one major drawback to this method, however. During the day hundreds of Big Pupils and teachers will get tripped and tangled up in all this string trailing around the school. As you wind the string up you will find them, still tangled up. They will then realize that you are the person responsible for the spot they are in, and they will bash you up.

3. Attach yourself to someone who has been there before and follow them around all day.

The drawback to this scheme is: the people who have been there before will be either Big Pupils or Teachers, and both of these will notice that you are in the wrong place (e.g. sitting in a sixth form class on Physics or next to the maths teacher in the Staff Room).

4. Walk around with a big sign around your neck saying 'I AM LOST. PLEASE HELP ME.'

Unfortunately, because all people at Big School are cruel and have a wicked sense of what they think is funny, they will pretend to show you the way, but actually they will give you directions to the nearest motorway.

Hints on how to deal with big pupils and mad teachers at big school

Surrender immediately. It will save you a lot of time.